Laura Comparetto
Illustrations by Irene de Prada

The Tail Of The Five Pupkateers

Bumblebee Books
London

BUMBLEBEE PAPERBACK EDITION

Copyright © Laura Comparetto 2021
Illustrations by Irene de Prada

A CIP catalogue record for this title is
available from the British Library.

ISBN: 978-1-83934-478-7

Bumblebee Books is an imprint of
Olympia Publishers.

First Published in 2021

Bumblebee Books
Tallis House
2 Tallis Street
London
EC4Y 0AB

Printed in Great Britain

www.olympiapublishers.com

Dedication

This book is dedicated to Melissa, Amy, Sonali, and Mike. Thank you for opening up your homes and heart to these precious pups. And to Bonnie, for traveling all the way to North Carolina to rescue them and bringing them all the way to New Jersey to where they will meet their forever families.

Five little puppies, all in a crate,
Huddled in the shelter, not knowing their fate

"What's going to happen to us?" one of them said.
"I can't help but feel we are in way over our heads."

These pups were siblings, two boys and three girls,
Each one of them precious, like little tiny pearls

One little boy, Roary was his name,
Had bright orange fur, the color of flame.
His hair was long and so very puffy,
He looked like a little walking cloud – he was that fluffy

Lucy and Lexi had fur of black and white.
One's hair was long, while the other's was short and tight.

Now these two puppies were quite special indeed,
for they were identical twins, a rare sight to perceive.
Known as Cody and Paisley, everything about them was the same.
From the little forward flop of their ears, to the shape of their frames.

Then one day, a nice lady stopped by their kennel.
She looked at them and spoke with a voice so gentle.
"Hello there, little ones. My name is Bonnie.
I'm going to bring you home with me and get you properly fed,
you're all way too scrawny."

These poor little puppies didn't know what to think.
They just stared at her, too scared to even blink.

The reason why, you ask? Because of a terrible first impression of mankind.
In a dark basement, inside a crate with their mother, they were confined.

The man who owned them was loud and mean,
He brought them to the shelter, barely even weaned.

He would bang on the crate if they made too much noise.
He would yell and shout at them, whenever he was annoyed.

But just as she promised, Bonnie took them far away.
There at the high-kill shelter, she didn't want them to stay.

Bonnie drove them for miles down the road,
Determined to bring home her precious load.

The next few days went by in a blur,
The siblings stuck close together, like burrs on their fur.

They arrived one day to a place so new,
It was crowded with other dogs, it looked like a zoo.

The five little puppies were then all showcased.
Alongside other dogs up for adoption, they were placed.

Hundreds of people came from far and wide,
To see the puppies that came from the countryside.

So many people wanted a pup to call their own.
But only a few were chosen, the decision set in stone.

Now, one year later,
Their lives couldn't be any greater!

The time for their reunion is coming very soon,
As a matter of fact, it'll be sometime this June!

By now I'm sure you're wondering, "Where are they now?"
Well, I'll tell you. Here's how.

Little Roary went off to a home in the mountains.
A picturesque landscape with lots of rivers and fountains.

His best friend is a cat named Pippy.
Though she loves him dearly, she can be a little snippy.

He loves to play with his soccer ball by bouncing it off his nose,

And playing with water – especially from the hose.

Roary loves to bark and play in the mud,

But he will only do it with Smitty, his best doggy bud!

Now Lucy and her family live near Long Beach.
She's a mama's girl, whom she clings to like a leech.

She loves nap times and scratches behind the ears,
But loud noises and new people are some of her biggest fears.

She loves to play with her water bowl by spilling it all over the floor,
A clean-up task that to her mom, has become quite the chore.

She loves to go swimming and running free in the woods.
Bully sticks and plush toys are her favorite of goods.

She likes visiting her grandparents who live way up north,
Then back to her beach house – she goes back and forth.

Shy little Lexi is all bark and no bite.
But any sudden movement will give her a fright.

She loves to play ball and chase a few birds,
The time for her to catch one though, has yet to occur.

Lexi's best friend is Olive, a dog who is quite pint-sized.
When their friendship was born, it was a bit of a surprise.

She loves to take naps, whether on a bed or rug,

And she won't let her dad walk by without a good morning hug!

Cody's new home is in a town nearby.
He likes other dogs, but is still very shy.

He's a big cuddle bug who loves to play with socks.
He'll dig through the laundry to find them, much to everyone's shock.

Cody is very spoiled for he demands kisses goodnight,
As well as being tucked in, nice and tight.

His girlfriend is Luna,

and his best friend is Buddy.
They run and play until they are both wet and muddy!

He loves stuffed toys, tug of war is his favorite game.

He enjoys wearing hats, he wears them without shame!

Dear sweet Paisley is in a home where she's loved to no end.

She loves going on walks and has made so many friends!

Her best friend is a dog named Stringer,

and her boyfriend's called Bert.
When they are together, they play in the pool and dig in the dirt.

When someone comes home from a long day at work,
She stands by the door, going absolutely berserk!

She gives 'creepy smiles' and big butt wiggles.
Both actions her family can't help but smile and giggle.

One thing you should know – Paisley is not a morning pup.
for when the sun starts to rise, she refuses to get up!

She is so still and silent, she acts like she's dead.
And if you try to wake her up, she won't even lift her head.

She loves to chew on bully sticks

and pull scrunchies from your hair,

But when she brings you a toy, she refuses to share.

It's hard to believe these pups share the same blood.
Then again, if they were all the same, wouldn't that be such a dud?

They are all so different, yet so much alike.
They love to splash in water, and go on hikes.

They all hate potatoes, but love to eat snow,
They'll jump and run it all day, even if it's thirty below!

It's so hard to imagine the time they were all small and weak.
For if they stayed at the shelter, their future looked bleak.

But their lives have now changed, their future is bright.
They inspire so much joy and love, their smiles full of delight.

And it's all thanks to that one special woman, who showed kindness and wisdom;
That every puppy was saved, by Bonnie's Animal Rescue Kingdom!

Wanna keep up with more of their adventures?
Follow them on their Instagram found below their bio!

Roary

Roary is currently living his best life in Boston. He is a big goofball who loves his human sister, Hannah, and enjoys digging in the sand at the beach. He is just now learning that it's fun to stick his head out the window, and he thinks candy canes are delicious. Just last year, Roary and Cody have reunited for the first time since they were adopted. Unsurprisingly, they recognized each other!

@goldencolliedog

LUCY

Lucy now resides in Staten Island. She adores her human siblings and doing yoga with Mom (her definition of yoga is sitting on the mat while Mom is using it). Her hobbies include napping in Mom's lap and playing in the kiddie pool with her human siblings.

⊙ @lucygoosey898

paisley

Paisley is living in New Jersey, not too far from where Cody lives and is planning to reunite with him soon. She is the only one of all her siblings who loves to go on walks. Paisley is a HUGE bed hog, absolutely loves to spread out and take up as much room as possible. She enjoys going to camp where she gains more and more confidence with each visit. She makes her family laugh every day and lives her life to the absolute fullest!

 @paiseep

Cody

Like Paisley, Cody also lives in New Jersey. He was adopted by one of the volunteers who works with Bonnie. At home, he likes to watch TV with his family. If his human doesn't share her snack with him, he will give her the silent treatment and ignore her the rest of the day. In the mornings, he loves to greet his family by bringing them one of his stuffed toys in his mouth! Overall, Cody is a happy-go-lucky dog who is loving life!

@dudenamedcody

Lexi

Lexi lives in New Jersey as well. She spends a lot of her time being active by playing and running in the yard. Lexi is affectionate with people she knows and she loves greeting her family in the morning with butt wags! She is not a huge fan of bath time, but will tolerate it - just long enough to get clean.

For more information about Bonnie's Animal Rescue Kingdom and dogs available for adoption, visit their Facebook or Instagram page at @bonniesanimalrescuekingdom to find out more!

About the Author

Having autism, I have always loved animals. That's part of the reason why I wrote this book. My main inspiration was my dog, Paisley, and the fact that she does and has the opportunity to reunite with all her siblings is amazing. Not a lot of dogs are able to do that.

Acknowledgements

Thank you Irene for all the hard work and time you put into creating these adorably fantastic drawings!

CPSIA information can be obtained
at www.ICGtesting.com
Printed in the USA
BVRC101305241121
622345BV00003BA/38